This edition published by Parragon Books Ltd in 2016

Parragon Books Ltd
Chartist House
15–17 Trim Street
Bath BA1 1HA, UK
www.parragon.com

Adapted by Jenny Dye
Illustrated by the Disney Storybook Artists

Designed by Vanessa Mee
Production by Charlotte McKillop

ISBN 978-1-4748-5290-6

Printed in China

Disney MOANA

Parragon

Bath • New York • Cologne • Melbourne • Delhi
Hong Kong • Shenzhen • Singapore

Moana was a little girl who lived with her family on the island of Motunui. Her home was a beautiful place, surrounded by a coral reef and shimmering blue seas.

Her father, Tui, was the chief of the island. Moana was destined to be chief too, one day.

Chief Tui cared very much about his people and made sure they were happy and safe. He didn't allow anyone to sail beyond the coral reef, where it might be dangerous.

After all, Motunui had everything the villagers needed. Who would ever want to leave?

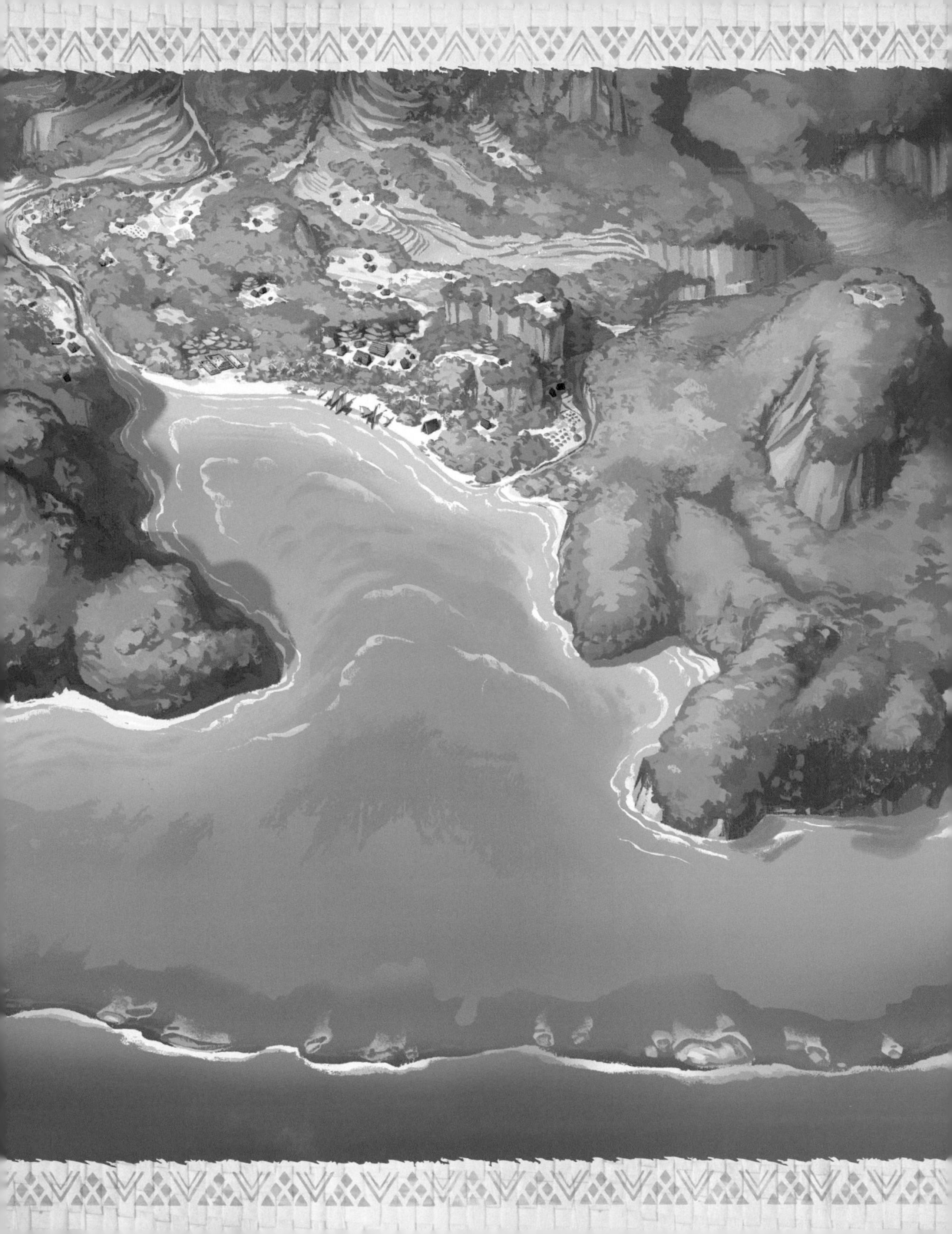

One day, Moana's Gramma Tala was telling a story to the children in the village.

"Long ago, there was an island goddess called Te Fiti," she began. "All life sprang from her heart. But one day, the giant demigod Maui took her heart. As Maui made off, a fire demon called Te Kā attacked him and the heart was lost to the sea forever."

The children were terrified – all except little Moana, who loved her grandma's stories.

Later that day, Moana was playing by the sea when the seawater magically rose up around her. She saw a spiral stone in the water and grasped it.

Just then, Chief Tui came looking for his daughter. As he picked up Moana, she dropped the stone.

Gramma Tala had been secretly watching from the bushes. She picked up the spiral stone before a wave washed it away.

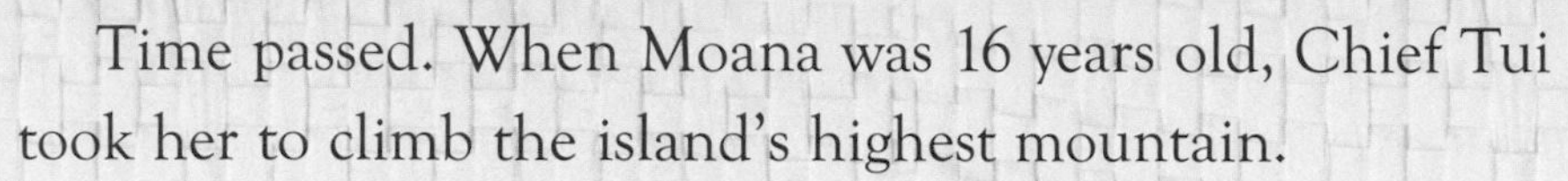

Time passed. When Moana was 16 years old, Chief Tui took her to climb the island's highest mountain.

"One day, you will add your stone to this mountain," he said, "and raise our whole island higher."

Tui told Moana how important it was for her to stay in the village and lead her people. Moana wanted to make her father proud, but she couldn't help wondering what might be out there, beyond the coral reef.

Later that day, Gramma Tala took Moana to a secret cave. Moana couldn't believe her eyes – the cave was filled with sailing boats! The boats belonged to their ancestors, who had been voyagers.

Gramma Tala explained that after Maui stole Te Fiti's heart, darkness took over the seas. The ancient chiefs stopped Moana's people from sailing to keep them safe.

"The darkness will spread to our island too, unless someone finds Maui and takes him to restore Te Fiti's heart," said Gramma Tala, "and the sea chose you." She gave the spiral stone to Moana. It was actually the heart of Te Fiti!

Soon after, Gramma Tala passed away. With her last breath, she told Moana to find Maui.

Moana took a little boat from the cave and set sail. But soon, a storm rose up. A giant wave crashed into her boat and everything faded to black.

When Moana woke up, she was on a strange beach.

Suddenly, Maui appeared. Moana had landed on his island!

Moana asked Maui to help her restore Te Fiti's heart, but he refused – he wanted to find his magical fishhook instead. The hook gave him the power to shape-shift into different animals, and he'd lost it in his battle with Te Kā. Maui trapped Moana in a cave and took her boat to go and search for his hook.

Moana was determined not to let Maui get away. She escaped from the cave and dived into the sea just as Maui set sail.

Suddenly, the sea pulled Moana under the water and placed her on the boat!

"You will put back the heart!" Moana said in her bravest voice, holding the spiral stone out to him. But Maui still refused to help her.

As Moana and Maui argued, spears started landing around them. They were being attacked by the Kakamora – little coconut-clad bandits.

Both Maui and Moana fought back against the tiny pirates until they were able to sail away.

Maui was impressed by Moana's bravery. He finally agreed to go with her to find Te Fiti, but said they would never succeed without his shape-shifting powers. They needed to find his fishhook first.

Maui was pretty sure who had his hook – Tamatoa, a giant crab who loved to collect treasures. Tamatoa lived in Lalotai, the realm of the monsters. By the next morning, Moana and Maui had reached the tall, rocky island that was the entrance to the realm.

The friends climbed up the steep rock and finally reached the peak. Moana and Maui each took a deep breath and jumped into the pitch-black hole that led into Lalotai.

In another world under the ocean, Moana and Maui found themselves in a huge, dark cavern.

Suddenly, Moana saw the hook, hidden in a pile of treasures. But just then, the ground rose up to reveal Tamatoa, who pinned Maui to the ground.

Thinking quickly, Moana held out the stone from her necklace.

Tamatoa scrambled to snatch the stone – he couldn't resist new treasures. Moana grabbed the hook, but then dropped the stone as she and Maui escaped.

"But – the heart!" cried Maui.

"He can have it, I've got this one," Moana whispered, as she opened her hand to reveal the real heart of Te Fiti. Moana had tricked Tamatoa with an ordinary rock!

Before the monster could attack, a geyser exploded underneath the two friends, launching them out through the top of the realm.

The pair travelled onwards to find Te Fiti. They were nearly there! But as they approached the island, Te Kā suddenly appeared out of a cloud of ash. Maui transformed himself into a hawk using his hook, but Te Kā knocked Maui from the sky.

Moana caught Maui in her boat and headed back towards Te Fiti. Maui tried to stop her: "We won't make it! Moana, turn back."

Te Kā's fist slammed downwards to crush their boat, but at the last second, Maui changed himself back into his human form and raised his hook to block Te Kā's fist.

A huge wave swept Moana, Maui and the boat far away. Moana wanted to go back, but Maui refused. Te Kā's blow had cracked the demigod's precious hook. Maui turned into a hawk again and angrily flew off.

Moana spoke to the sea with tears in her eyes. "I couldn't make it. You'll have to choose someone else," she said, heartbroken. Then she held the heart out to the sea and a wave reached up and took it back.

Just then, the spirit of Gramma Tala appeared and said that she would always be with Moana, whatever she decided to do.

Suddenly, hundreds of ghostly canoes emerged from the sea, and a chorus of voices rose up. "Know who you are," the voices chanted. They were the spirits of Moana's voyaging ancestors.

Moana realized that she would be the one to restore Te Fiti's heart. She dived over the side of her boat and took the heart back from the sea bed.

Back on her boat, Moana headed towards Te Fiti once again. Te Kā wanted to stop her. But just before Te Kā struck Moana, Maui appeared out of nowhere to take the blow!

While Maui and Te Kā battled on, Moana reached Te Fiti. But something was terribly wrong: the island was just an empty crater, and the goddess was nowhere to be seen.

Te Kā swooped down in front of Moana, but the demon no longer seemed frightening. Trusting her instincts, Moana reached out and placed the heart into Te Kā's chest. She watched as the face of the lava monster transformed. Now that the goddess's heart was restored, she was changing back to her true self.

Te Fiti opened her hand to reveal Maui's hook, fixed – she had forgiven him. Te Fiti's island exploded with flowers and came back to life, at last.

Back on Motunui, Tui was very worried about his missing daughter. But then Moana appeared on the horizon, and Chief Tui and the villagers of Motunui were overjoyed.

Moana had restored Te Fiti's heart, which meant her people could sail safely across the sea again, just as they had done long ago.

Moana finally knew who she was – the next great explorer, destined to lead her tribe on amazing new adventures.

SPACE

Asteroids and Comets

Ian Graham

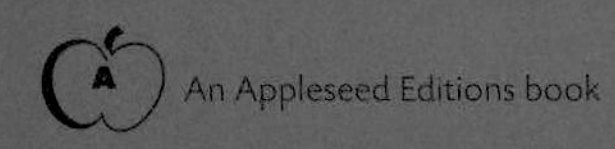

Franklin Watts
First published in Great Britain in 2016
by The Watts Publishing Group

Designed by Guy Callaby
Edited by Mary-Jane Wilkins

Picture acknowledgements
t = top, b = bottom, l = left, r = right
page 1 Michael Knight; 2-3 Artur Kamalov;
4 Tom De Spiegelaere/all Thinkstock;
5 Valerio Pardi; 6 Linda Brotkorb/both
Shutterstock; 7 Yuriy Mazur; 8t ESA/Max-Planck-Institute for Solar System Research,
b Digital Vision; 9l NASA, r Halley
Multicolor Camera Team, Giotto Project,
ESA; 10-11 artwork by Pat Rawlings
Courtesy of NASA/JPL/UMD; 11br NASA/
JPL-Caltech/UMD; 12 Stocktrek Images/
Thinkstock; 13 NASA; 14 taeya18; 15 Tim
Fan/both Thinkstock; 16 Pichugin Dmitry;
17 DAIVI; 18 NatUlrich; 19 razlomov;
20-21 puchan, 21b Action Sports
Photography/all Shutterstock
Cover t Andrea Danti, b Ig0rZh/
both Thinkstock

Dewey number 523.4'4-dc23
HB ISBN 978 1 4451 4908 0

Printed in China

Franklin Watts
An imprint of
Hachette Children's Group
Part of The Watts Publishing Group
Carmelite House
50 Victoria Embankment
London EC4Y 0DZ

An Hachette UK Company
www.hachette.co.uk

www.franklinwatts.co.uk

Contents

SPACE ROCKS

Look up into a clear night sky and you'll see stars shining brightly, but there are a lot more things in space.

LEFTOVERS

When the Sun and our world were made, lots of pieces of rock and ice were left over. Some of them are still flying around in space today.

Rocks of all shapes and sizes are flying around in space.

Big and small

Space rocks up to about the size of a small car are called meteoroids. Bigger rocks are called asteroids. Some space rocks have ice mixed with the rock. These icy rocks are called comets.

Comets are made of rock and ice, like dusty snowballs.

SPOTLIGHT ON SPACE

WHERE ARE THEY?

Most space rocks are too small, too dark and too far away to be seen, but you might be lucky enough to see a comet.

Comets

If you see a fuzzy bright ball in the sky with a long bright tail, or two tails, you've spotted a comet.

Space mountains

A comet is a ball of ice and rock as big as a mountain. If it comes close to the Sun, it becomes brighter and easier to see.

When a comet warms up, dust and gas fly off it.

GROWING TAILS

The dust and gas flying off a comet form a big cloud called a coma around the comet. Then the coma stretches out to make the comet's tails.

A comet has a bright dust tail and a blue tail made of gas.

SPOTLIGHT ON SPACE

WHERE DO THEY COME FROM?

Comets come from two places far away from the Sun called the scattered disc and the Oort Cloud. Just a few comets visit us from these faraway places.

Halley's Comet

The most famous comet is called Halley's Comet. It appears in the sky every 75 or 76 years.

Round the Sun

Comets go round and round the Sun. Some take thousands of years to make the trip. Others take less than 100 years. Halley's Comet was here in 1986 and should be back again in 2061.

Halley's Comet is bright enough to see without a telescope.

Visiting Halley

The last time Halley's Comet appeared, five unmanned spacecraft were sent to visit it. A spacecraft called *Giotto* took some amazing close-up photographs of the comet.

***Giotto* flew through the cloud of dust around Halley's Comet.**

Spotlight on Space

A Lumpy Rock

Giotto's photographs show a big lumpy rock with jets of gas and dust flying out of it. The icy rock at the centre of a comet is called the nucleus.

Deep Impact

Scientists wanted to know what comets are like inside, so they sent a spacecraft to find out. It was called *Deep Impact*.

Comet hunting

Deep Impact carried a heavy block of metal called an impactor. When it got close to a comet called Tempel 1, it sent the impactor flying towards the comet.

SPOTLIGHT ON SPACE

ISLAND IN SPACE

Comet Tempel 1 is about the same size as a small island. This island in space takes 5½ years to travel round the Sun.

MAKING A CLOUD

Deep Impact's impactor hit comet Tempel 1. It made a hole in the comet and sent a cloud of dusty pieces of rock, gas and ice flying out into space.

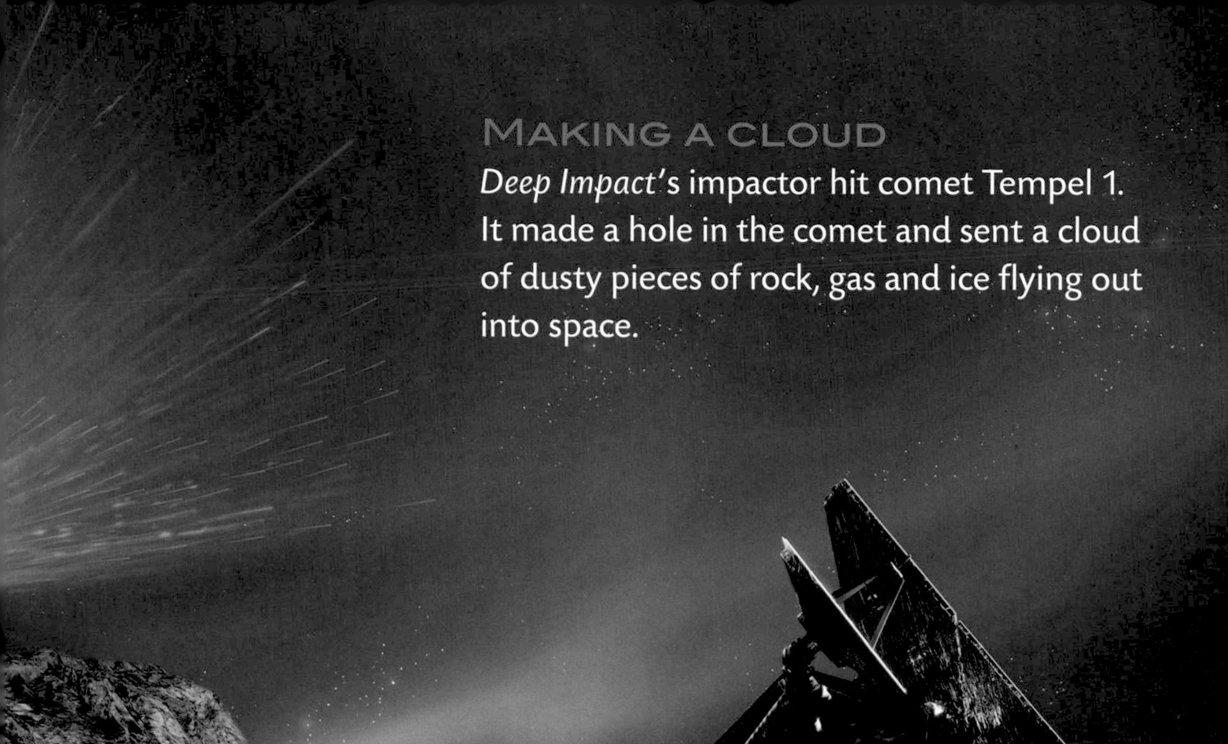

Deep Impact ***took a picture of its impactor hitting comet Tempel 1.***

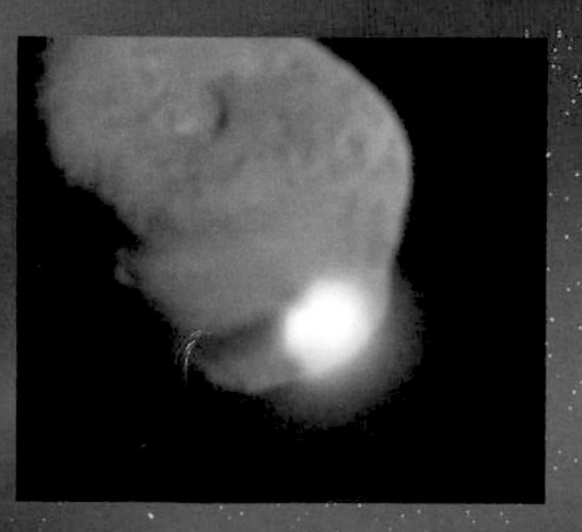

Catching Comets

Two space missions set out to learn more about comets by testing pieces of them. One mission even brought some comet dust back to Earth.

Collecting dust

The *Stardust* spacecraft met a comet called Wild-2 as it sped through space. It caught some of the dust flying off the comet and then headed back to Earth.

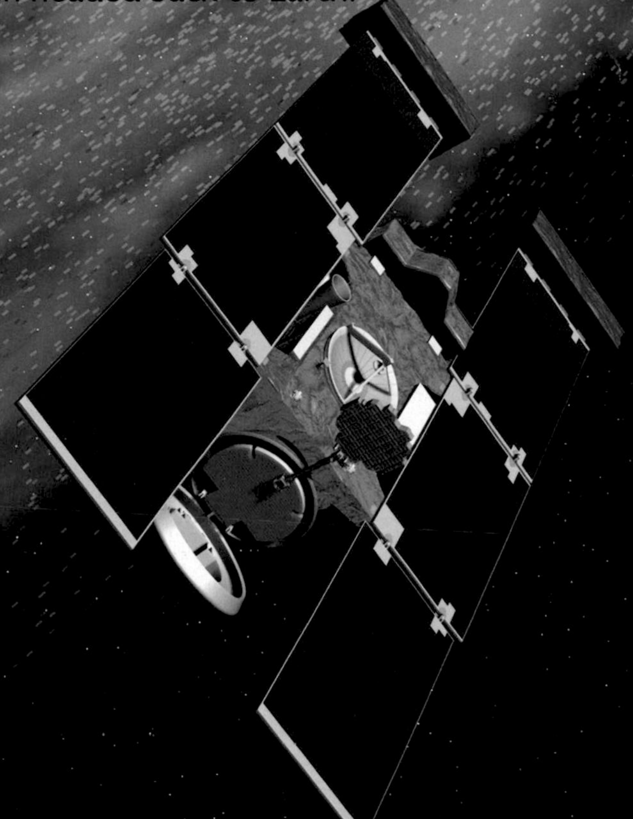

The* Stardust *spacecraft races towards comet Wild-2.

COMING HOME

As *Stardust* flew past Earth, it dropped a capsule with the precious comet dust inside. The capsule popped out a parachute and floated down to a safe landing.

SPOTLIGHT ON SPACE

LANDING ON A COMET

The Rosetta *spacecraft carried a tiny craft called* Philae *to a comet called Churyumov-Gerasimenko. Philae's job is to land on the comet and find out what it is made of.*

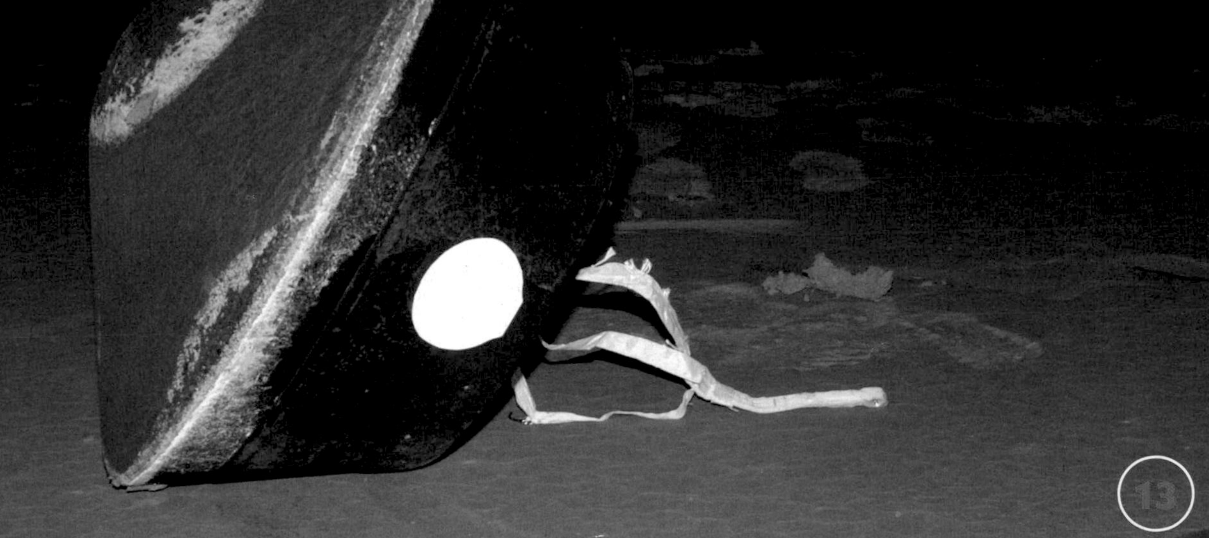

***Stardust's* capsule sits on the ground after coming back from space.**

SHOOTING STARS

On a clear night, you might see a streak of light in the sky. It's called a shooting star, but it isn't a star.

BURNING UP

When a small piece of rock, a meteoroid, flies into the air around Earth, it heats up until it glows and then changes to gas. This is the streak of light you see.

A meteoroid comes to a fiery end as a meteor, or shooting star.

Meteors streak through the sky during a meteor shower.

Meteor showers

On some nights of the year, there are lots of meteors. These meteor showers happen when the Earth travels through a trail of dust left behind by a comet.

Tiny but bright

SPOTLIGHT ON SPACE

Most meteors, or shooting stars, are no bigger than your fingertip. Some are as small as a grain of sand. We see them because they glow brightly as they burn up.

Meteorites

The smallest space rocks burn up in the air, but bigger rocks fall all the way down to the ground. They are called meteorites.

Big and small

Meteorites can be as small as a pebble or much bigger. Luckily for us, most meteorites are very small and they fall in places where there are no people.

This meteorite weighing 54 tonnes was found in Namibia, Africa.

STONE AND IRON

There are three types of meteorites. One is made of stone. The second is made of metal, mostly iron. The third type is a mixture of these two, called stony-irons.

A huge fiery meteorite falls into the sea.

SPOTLIGHT ON SPACE

HISTORY LESSON

Meteorites are interesting because they come from a time long ago, before the Earth was born. We can learn more about that time by studying meteorites.

ASTEROIDS

Asteroids are big lumpy pieces of rock and metal. Millions of them travel round the Sun far away from Earth.

WHERE ARE THEY?

Nearly all asteroids are in the gap between two planets, Mars and Jupiter. This wide band of space is called the Asteroid Belt.

Hundreds of new asteroids are found in the Asteroid Belt every year.

Changing direction

Sometimes, asteroids crash into each other and fly off in new directions. Every now and then, an asteroid is sent flying towards the Sun. It might even fly past Earth.

Spotlight on space

NEAR-Shoemaker

A spacecraft called NEAR-Shoemaker *was sent to study an asteroid called Eros. At the end of its mission, scientists managed to land the spacecraft on the asteroid – something it wasn't designed to do!*

All the asteroids joined together would make something smaller than the Moon.

CRASHING TO EARTH

The Earth has been hit by asteroids and comets in the past and it will be hit again in the future. Scientists are looking for anything that might be coming towards us.

Millions of years ago, giant asteroids crashed into Earth.

DINOSAUR KILLER

Dinosaurs lived on Earth for 160 million years. They died out 65 million years ago when a huge asteroid hit Earth. A lot of other animals died out too.

SPOTLIGHT ON SPACE

DISASTER

If a giant comet or asteroid hit Earth, soil and rock would be thrown up into the air. On the ground it would be as dark as night for months.

SAVING EARTH

If a comet or asteroid is spotted heading for Earth, it could be pushed away by a rocket. Spaceflights to comets and asteroids help scientists plan how to do it.

This huge crater in Arizona was made by an asteroid 50,000 years ago.

GLOSSARY

asteroid A piece of rock or metal, or a mixture of the two, bigger than a car and smaller than the Moon, flying round the Sun.

coma The cloud of ice and dust around the head of a comet.

comet A ball of ice and rock dust travelling round the Sun.

Earth Our home in space, the third planet from the Sun. One of eight planets travelling round the Sun.

impactor A small spacecraft or other object that is sent to crash into something at high speed.

Jupiter The fifth planet from the Sun and the biggest of the eight planets that travel round the Sun.

Mars The fourth planet from the Sun, also called the Red Planet because of its colour.

meteor A streak of light in the sky caused by a meteoroid flying into the air from space and heating up until it glows. Also called a shooting star.

meteorite A piece of rock or metal, or a mixture of the two, that comes from space, travels through the air and lands on the ground.

meteoroid A piece of rock or metal, or a mixture of the two, up to the size of a car, travelling through space.

nucleus The solid part of a comet, made of rock dust and ice.

planet One of the eight worlds that travel round the Sun. There are planets travelling round other stars too.

shooting star Another name for a meteor.

spacecraft A machine that leaves Earth and travels through space. Some spacecraft have people inside. Unmanned spacecraft have no one inside.

space mission A spaceflight. It begins with a rocket launching a spacecraft. Then the spacecraft, or the people inside it, carry out the work they have been sent into space to do. Most unmanned spacecraft stay in space at the end of their mission. Other spacecraft come back to Earth.

Sun The star closest to us.

WEBSITES

http://starchild.gsfc.nasa.gov/docs/StarChild/solar_system_level2/meteoroids.html
Information about meteoroids from the US space agency NASA.

http://solarsystem.nasa.gov/planets/profile.cfm?Object=Asteroids&Display=Kids
Find out how much you would weigh if you stood on an asteroid.

http://www.sciencekids.co.nz/sciencefacts/space/asteroids.html
Facts about asteroids.

http://www.esa.int/esaKIDSen/SEMN99WJD1E_OurUniverse_0.html
Lots of information about comets, meteors and meteorites from the European Space Agency (ESA).

http://www.sciencekids.co.nz/sciencefacts/space/meteoroids.html
Lots of meteoroid facts.

http://www.nhm.ac.uk/kids-only/earth-space/meteorites/index.html
Find out more about meteorites from the Natural History Museum in London.

http://www.sciencekids.co.nz/sciencefacts/space/comets.html
Lots of comet facts, including the comet that crashed into the planet Jupiter.

INDEX